JUDGE DR[EDD]

C000217580

Virtual Unreality

Script	J. WAGNER
Art	J. BURNS
Lettering	T. FRAME

CONTROL! SIDE DOOR TO THE KEATING STREET GALLERY IS LYING OPEN. I'M GOING TO CHECK IT OUT.

AHH! THERE YOU ARE! I'VE BEEN EXPECTING YOU!

THAT SO? YOU ARE —?

PALLET, SIR. AUGUST PALLET. MASTER PAINTER.

THESE LOOK LIKE FORGERIES TO ME.

COPIES, SIR! MARVELLOUS — PERFECT — BUT COPIES, NO MORE. EACH BEARING MY OWN SIGNATURE!

AND SHOULD THE PURCHASER WISH TO REMOVE MY NAME AND REPLACE IT WITH PICASSO — DALI — REMBRANDT — MICHELANGELO — WHY, HARDLY MY CONCERN!

YOU MISSED A BIT.

HOW OBSERVANT YOU ARE! I KNEW I HAD CHOSEN THE RIGHT MAN!

YOU SEE, VARIOUS PARTS OF MY WORK HAVE BEEN **DISAPPEARING** -- MONA LISA'S SMILE -- VAN DYCK'S BEARD -- POOR VINCENT'S SUNFLOWERS -- TO NAME BUT A FEW.

A CLEAR CASE OF THEFT, SIR! THAT'S WHY I BROUGHT YOU HERE -- TO INVESTIGATE!

YOU BROUGHT ME?

YES INDEED! YOU SEE -- I'M PAINTING YOU IN. JUST ADDING THE FINISHING TOUCH.

I'M SURE IT'S ONE OF MY BROOD WHO'S DOING IT -- PROBABLY ONE OF THE SURREALISTS. THEY TAKE SUCH DELIGHT IN THE UNEXPECTED.

YOU'RE NOT MAKING A LOT OF SENSE, PALLET -- BUT I SUPPOSE AS LONG AS YOU DON'T START CREATING A NUISANCE...

JUST KEEP YOUR DOOR LOCKED IN FUTURE OR I'LL HAVE TO COME DOWN ON YOU HARD.

HUH?

OKAY, I'M DREAMIN', RIGHT...

LITTLE CREEP MUST'VE HIT ME WITH SOME FUNNY GAS--

MIGHT AS WELL PLAY THIS OUT TO THE END...

BANG! CLANNG! KLANK!

S. DALI

SCRAP

WOTCHER, ME OLD CHINA! BLIMEY, IS THIS YOUR LUCKY DAY! HAVE I GOT SOME BARGAINS FOR YOU!

THERE--TAKE YER PICK! BUNCH NICE SUNFLOWERS-- FIVE AN' A TANNER! 'OW ABOUT VAN DYCK'S BEARD-- THAT'LL PUT SOME 'AIRS ON YER CHEST!

OR A STUBBS 'ORSE! 'OW ABOUT A NICE STUBBS 'ORSE? TELL YER WOT, I'LL EVEN FROW IN A FLAMIN' HAYWAIN WIV IT! THERE YOU ARE, CAN'T SAY FAIRER THAN THAT!

STOLEN PROPERTY, IF I'M ANY JUDGE!

WEREN'T MY FAULT, MATE. I DIDN'T NICK THE STUFF--DIDN'T KNOW IT WAS 'OT. BOUGHT IT OFF THEM...THEM WEIRD-LOOKIN' GEEZERS --TH-THE PICASSOS...

PICASSO, HUH? RIGHT! WE'RE GETTING SOMEWHERE!

WHICH WAY OUT?

HMMM...

MAKES AS MUCH SENSE AS ANYTHING ELSE!

RUBENS

NOT THERE...

DROKK!

HERE WE ARE!

PICASSO

THE END

THE DAYS PASS WITH ALL THE BREATHLESS EXCITEMENT OF A LONG, DRAWN-OUT DEATH RATTLE AS VEEBLESUMP AND HIS MINIONS ANNEX THE AIRWAVES...

B-SUCK-B

ATTENTION, VIDDERS! REPLACING 'BEVERLEY HILLBILLIES 90210' THIS WEEK, WE'VE AN EXTENDED EDITION OF 'DESCALING KETTLES THE JIM BOWEN WAY!'

AND FOLLOWING OUR RIP-ROARING 1923 UKRANIAN DOCUMENTARY ON SOIL EROSION THERE'S ANOTHER CHANCE TO SEE LAST NIGHT'S 'GREAT PARTY POLITICAL BROADCASTS' OMNIBUS!

SURE ENOUGH, THE VIEWING PUBLIC ARE NO MATCH FOR THE **TIDAL WAVE** OF **CRASHING TEDIUM** SPEWING FORTH INTO THEIR HOMES!

NORMAN! M-ME **CEREBRAL CORTEX**— IT'S **LIQUEFYING!**

G-GOT TO REACH THE **REMOTE!** YET SOMEHOW, STRANGELY, I JUST CAN'T BE BOTHERED!

ZZZZZZZ!

--NOW, JOHN MAJOR IS THIS WEEK'S GUEST ON 'DESERT ISLAND WALLPAPER PATTERNS...'

GRUD ON A GREENIE-- THIS IS...ER...UM... **TERRIBLE!** ALL OUR POWER AND WE CAN'T SAVE THEM!

PERHAPS WE **CAN**, BURT...

...IT SEEMS THE WALLS OF OUR CELL ARE MADE OF **PLASTIC**-!

Covers of 1992

THE DROIDS DECIDE

BORAG WOSSNAME,

Every year, Tharg the Discerning calls upon his script and art droids to cast a rheumy eye over the past year's 2000 AD covers and select just one as a personal favourite. Here are the results, along with a pithy comment from each of the droids concerned. If you violently disagree with any of the choices, complain to the droids, not Tharg.

SPLUNDIG VUR THINGUMMY

Tharg

PETER HOGAN *(Script Droid)*
Prog 800 by Sean Phillips
Because: "of the imaginative use of colour which brings the town to life - bright lights, Mega-City!"

JOHN RIDGWAY *(Art Droid)*
Prog 804 by John Ridgway
Because: "I was paid for it!"

17

CHRIS WESTON *(Art Droid)*
Prog 775 by Cliff Robinson
Because: "Cliff's artwork is so gloriously clean you could eat your dinner off it."

JOHN SMITH *(Script Droid)*
Prog 797 by Yeowell/Cook/Curley
Because: "If you stare at it long enough through squinted eyes it gives you a funny tingly feeling in your prostate (I don't know - maybe it's just me)."

PAUL MARSHALL *(Art Droid)*
Prog 796 by Carlos Ezquerra
Because: "I think Carlos is a very good drawrer."

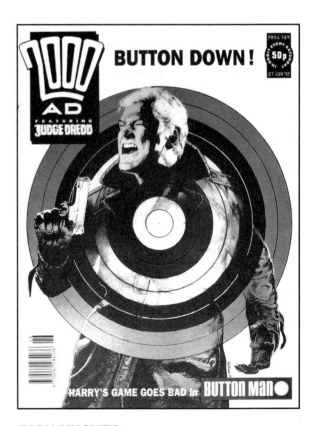

RIAN HUGHES *(Art Droid)*
Prog 789 by Arthur Ranson
Because: "Composition is king, simple is beautiful, and white is my second favourite colour (after Pantone 333)."

BISH-OP *(Editorial Droid)*
Prog 815 by Colin Macneil
Because: "it's simple, eye-catching and
Christmas-sy - but not too festive (creeps!)."

DAVE HILL *(Art Droid)*
Prog 811 by Mick Austin
Because: "I admire the subtle and economical use
of colour which emphasises the brilliantly painted,
menacing figure of Finn, caught for a split second
in the moonlight. Smashing!"

ALAN McKENZIE *(Script Droid)*
Prog 795 by Simon Harrison/Gina Hart
Because: "It's what Bradley is all about and I
like white background on covers."

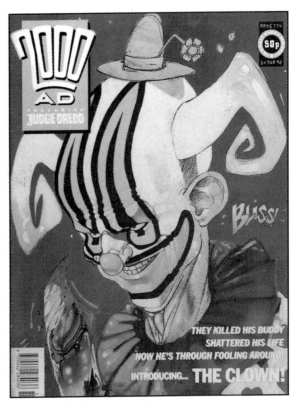

JOHN TOMLINSON *(Script Droid)*
Prog 774 by Robert Bliss
Because: "It speaks to me. No it does, really. I
don't have to listen though - not while I'm wearing
the bacofoil smock the Atlantonauts gave me!"

MAC-1 *(Editorial Droid)*
Prog 789 by Arthur Ranson
Because: "it's white on target (or should I say, white on the *Button*?)

MICK AUSTIN *(Art Droid)*
Prog 792 by Steve Yeowell
Because: "It's a happy, jolly picture and he looks kinda smug."

GREG STAPLES *(Art Droid)*
Prog 802 by Cliff Robinson
Because: "I like typical Dredd poses and I wish I'd thought of this one first. Can I go now?"

CYB-AUD *(Editorial Droid)*
Prog 801 by Carl Critchlow
Because: "It delivers maximum shock impact and serves as a reminder of my need to visit the dentist regularly!"

TYRANNY REX

BITTER FRUIT

"BLESS ME, O LORD AND MARTYR, THAT I MIGHT FIND GRACE AND HUMILITY IN THY PRESENCE."

FOR I HAVE SEEN A BRIGHT AND SHINING HUNGER THAT THREATENS TO DEVOUR US ALL...

...AND ONLY WITH THY LOVING GRACE WILL WE OVERCOME IT.

IT'S BEEN SEVEN YEARS SINCE TYRANNY JOINED THE CHURCH OF THE THIRD IMMACULUM.

SHE'S NEVER BEEN AS FRIGHTENED IN HER LIFE.

SOMETHING BAD'S COMING.

SHE CAN FEEL IT.

TYRANNY! SISTER TYRANNY!

COME QUICKLY!

IT'S VENETZ.

I...I THINK SHE'S GOING TO DIE...

2000 AD Credit Card
Script JOHN SMITH
Art PAUL MARSHALL
Lettering ANNIE PARKHOUSE

21

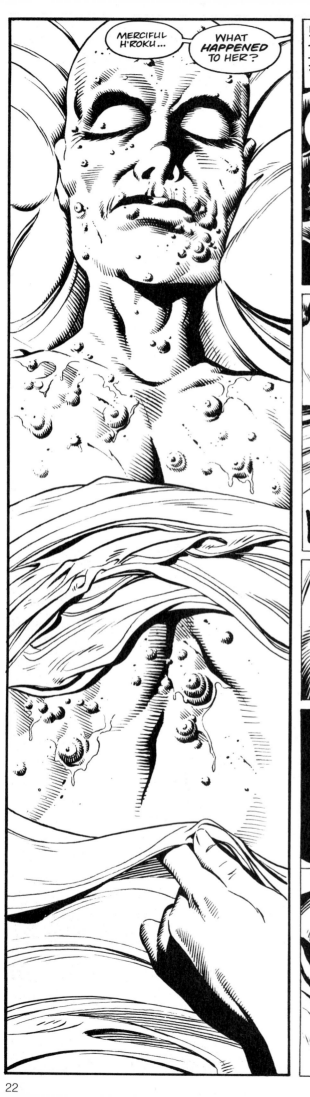

MERCIFUL H'ROKU...

WHAT *HAPPENED* TO HER?

W-WE WERE OUT IN YALLERY FIELD, ABOUT TO HARVEST THE FRUIT —POMEGRANATES AND JACKMELONS— AND THEY JUST...

THEY CAME OUT OF NOWHERE... *THOUSANDS* OF THEM...

WHAT *DID?* WHAT ARE YOU *TALKING* ABOUT?

OUR SISTER IS TALKING ABOUT *THESE*, CHILD... LILLIM.

BUT THE LILLIM HAVE ALWAYS BEEN SUCH *SWEET* CREATURES. THEY'VE NEVER HARMED ANYONE BEFORE.

THIS ONE LOOKS ALMOST *DERANGED*...

AND THERE ARE THOUSANDS MORE OUT IN THE FIELDS. ALL OF THEM *BERSERK*, ALL GONE SUDDENLY *WILD*... MAKING IT IMPOSSIBLE FOR US TO GATHER IN OUR CROPS.

HOW ARE WE TO SURVIVE THE WINTER IF WE MISS THE HARVEST? WHAT WILL WE EAT *THEN*?

SHE KNOWS WHAT'S GOING TO COME NEXT, AND WHEN HIGH SISTER KEERA FINALLY ASKS HER, TYRANNY TURNS AND NODS AND SAYS

YES. OF COURSE I'LL GO. I WOULD BE *HONOURED*.

SHE FEELS SICK TO THE PIT OF HER STOMACH.

TYRANNY REX

BITTER FRUIT

"BLESS ME, O LORD AND MARTYR, THAT I MIGHT FIND GRACE AND HUMILITY IN THY PRESENCE."

FOR I HAVE SEEN A BRIGHT AND SHINING HUNGER THAT THREATENS TO DEVOUR US ALL...

...AND ONLY WITH THY LOVING GRACE WILL WE OVERCOME IT.

IT'S BEEN SEVEN YEARS SINCE TYRANNY JOINED THE CHURCH OF THE THIRD IMMACULUM.

SHE'S NEVER BEEN AS FRIGHTENED IN HER LIFE.

SOMETHING BAD'S COMING.

SHE CAN FEEL IT.

TYRANNY! SISTER TYRANNY!

COME QUICKLY!

IT'S VENETZ.

I...I THINK SHE'S GOING TO DIE...

2000 AD Credit Card

Script JOHN SMITH

Art PAUL MARSHALL

Lettering ANNIE PARKHOUSE

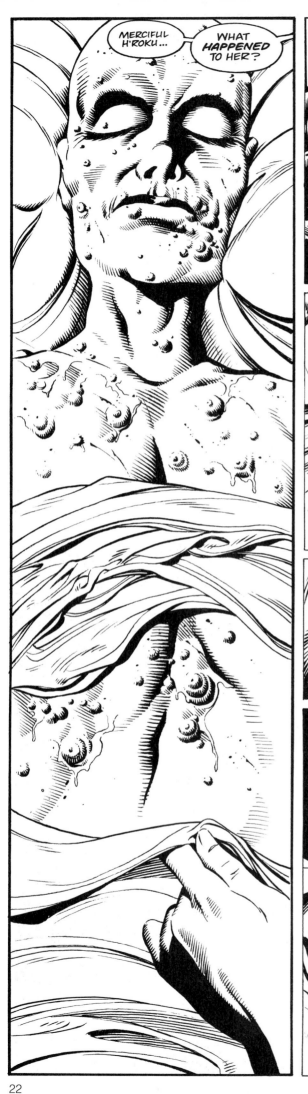

MERCIFUL H'ROKU...

WHAT *HAPPENED* TO HER?

W-WE WERE OUT IN YALLERY FIELD, ABOUT TO HARVEST THE FRUIT —POMEGRANATES AND JACKMELONS— AND THEY JUST...

THEY CAME OUT OF NOWHERE... THOUSANDS OF THEM...

WHAT DID? WHAT ARE YOU *TALKING* ABOUT?

OUR SISTER IS TALKING ABOUT *THESE,* CHILD... LILLIM.

KVZWVZVKKVVZ

KKZV

KZVZZKVZ   KVZVOVZVZZ

BUT THE *LILLIM* HAVE ALWAYS BEEN SUCH *SWEET* CREATURES. THEY'VE NEVER HARMED ANYONE BEFORE.

THIS ONE LOOKS ALMOST *DERANGED*...

AND THERE ARE THOUSANDS MORE OUT IN THE FIELDS. ALL OF THEM *BERSERK,* ALL GONE SUDDENLY *WILD*... MAKING IT IMPOSSIBLE FOR US TO GATHER IN OUR CROPS.

HOW ARE WE TO SURVIVE THE WINTER IF WE MISS THE HARVEST? WHAT WILL WE EAT *THEN?*

SHE KNOWS WHAT'S GOING TO COME NEXT, AND WHEN HIGH SISTER KEERA FINALLY ASKS HER, TYRANNY TURNS AND NODS AND SAYS

YES. OF COURSE I'LL GO. I WOULD BE *HONOURED.*

SHE FEELS SICK TO THE PIT OF HER STOMACH.

HALLOWE'EN, 1963.

BUT MUM, THE GRIM REAPER LOOKS *DAFT* WEARING A SCARF...

I DON'T CARE. YOU'RE NOT GOING *WITHOUT* IT.

THE JOURNAL OF LUKE KIRBY
Trick or Treat

'BYE, BOYS. DON'T BE TOO LATE.

YEAH, DON'T WANT TO CATCH YOUR *DEATH* OF COLD.

OH, VERY FUNNY!

SO... WHERE'RE WE GOING TO *START*?

TRICK OR TREEEAT!

NOT ROUND HERE.

2000 AD Credit Card
Script A. McKENZIE
Art J. RIDGWAY
Lettering ANNIE. P

LET'S GO OVER *WOODHILL* WAY. WE'LL HAVE ALL THOSE STREETS TO *OURSELVES*...

YEAH...

SO WE WORKED UP ONE SIDE OF WOODHILL STREET AND DOWN THE OTHER.

DOING PRETTY WELL, AS IT WENT.

UNTIL WE CAME TO **THE HOUSE**...

WELL? WHAT D'YOU THINK?

AFTER THE NIGHT WALKER * AFFAIR, THE HOUSE HAD BEEN BOUGHT AND FIXED UP BY AN ELDERLY LADY, MATILDA KANE.

THE KIDS IN THE AREA THOUGHT SHE HAD TO BE A WITCH FOR WANTING TO LIVE HERE, BUT I KNEW THE EVIL WASN'T IN HER...

* THARGNOTE: SEE **2000 AD** PROGS 800-812.

IT WAS **THE HOUSE**.

GO ON, LUKE. GO KNOCK ON THE DOOR...

IF I'D HAD ANY SENSE, I'D HAVE TOLD THEM TO KNOCK ON THE DOOR THEMSELVES...

THEN AGAIN...

ERR... TRICK OR TREAT?

TRICK!

AAH...

OH, COME ON, LUKE.

YOU'RE THE LAST OF THE KIRBYS...

SURELY YOU CAN MANAGE ONE LITTLE MAGICK TRICK FOR ME?

WELL, IF YOU WON'T DO ONE FOR *ME*...

I'LL JUST HAVE TO DO ONE FOR *YOU*.

I THOUGHT SHE WAS JUST HAVING ME ON. PULLING MY LEG FOR HALLOWE'EN.

SHE WAS VERY PRETTY. JUST A LITTLE WEIRD.

HERE, LUKE. LET'S WATCH SOME TV.

DOES THIS MAN LOOK A LITTLE FAMILIAR?

COULDN'T BE YOUR *FATHER*, COULD IT?

I WENT BACK TO THE HOUSE THE NEXT DAY. I WANTED TO KNOW WHO THE YOUNG GIRL WAS, WHETHER SHE REALLY DID KNOW ANYTHING ABOUT MY FATHER.

SHE WASN'T THERE, OF COURSE, BUT SOMEONE ELSE WAS.

HALLO, YOUNG MAN. WANT TO LOOK AROUND NOW OLD AUNT TILLY'S GONE? HELP YOURSELF. I'M NOT STAYING.

GONE? YOU MEAN SHE DIED?

LAST MONDAY. SHE LEFT ME THIS PLACE. SO I'M JUST HAVING A SCOUT AROUND TO SEE IF THERE'S ANYTHING I WANT BEFORE I PUT IT ON THE MARKET.

SHE WAS A STRANGE OLD GIRL. BIT OF A CORKER WHEN SHE WAS YOUNG, THOUGH.

THAT'S HER WHEN SHE WAS NINETEEN.

34

THE JOURNAL OF LUKE KIRBY RETURNS TO 2000 AD WEEKLY SOON.

THARG'S FUTURE-SHOCKS

CONVERSATION PIECE!

IT'S VERY IMPRESSIVE. OUR 3SPOUSE SAW ONE AT CELEBRATIONINGS, SUGGESTED I COME TO BEHOLD IT.

OF COURSE, MAKING THEM IS ONLY A HOBBY. BUT I DO LIKE TO THINK IT IS AN ORIGINAL ART FORM.

DO YOU CREATE THE ENTIRETY YOURSELF?

OH INDEED NO. I PURCHASE JUNKED PLANETS IN BULK. I USED TO MAKE MY OWN, BUT WELL, WAITING FOR DUST MOLECULES TO CONGEAL IS SO **DULL**, WOULDN'T YOU SAY?

ANYWAY, THE EFFECTS I AM PROUDEST OF CONCERN THE **DETAIL** WORK.

YES, MINUTIAE WORKMANSHIP. 3SPOUSE MENTIONED SUCH TO ME. IT IS EFFECTED BY YOURSELF?

GOODNESS, NO. IT'S **FAR** TOO SMALL FOR THAT. HERE, LOOK AT SOME OF THESE AREAS... LOVELY STUFF, ISN'T IT?

YOU SEE IT'S ALL BUILT BY MEANS OF **HOMUNCULI** — SUCH **TINY** CREATURES YOU WOULD SCARCELY CREDIT IT!

ALL **I** DO IS INTRODUCE LIFE-FORCE TO THE PLANET, WAIT WHILE IT EVOLVES INTO THESE HOMUNCULI...

SCRIPT ROBOT	ART ROBOT	LETTERING ROBOT
NEIL GAIMAN	DAVID WYATT	TOM FRAME

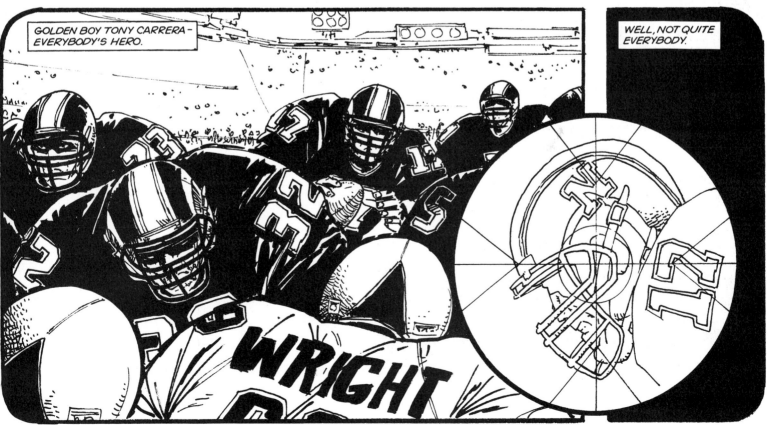

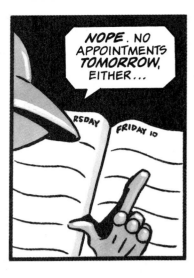

THE HOTEL REGISTER SAID A MR AND MRS ENRICO DEL SMITH WERE STAYING IN ROOM 459.

I WAS PRETTY SURE IT WAS THEM.

WHO IS IT?

ROOM SERVICE, MA'AM.

WE DIDN'T ORDER ANYTHING!

BRATTAATTATTER!

46

ONCE UPON A TIME THERE WAS A **CLOWN**.

WHO WAS STUCK INSIDE A STORY.

THE CLOWN WAS CONDEMNED TO REPEAT THE SAME **PATHETIC** PLOT WITH MINOR VARIATIONS, OVER AND OVER AGAIN UNTIL IT WAS ALMOST IMPOSSIBLE TO DISTINGUISH HIM FROM A **CLICHE**.

NOW THE CLOWN WAS **NOT** STUPID. HE KNEW THAT HE WAS STUCK INSIDE A STORY, HE ALSO KNEW THERE WAS REASON FOR HIS BEING HERE IN PLACE AND TIME.

AND HE DID NOT FANCY BECOMING A CLICHE.

The CLOWN

2000 AD Credit Card

Script **IGOR GOLDKIND**

Art **GREG STAPLES**

Lettering **ANNIE PARKHOUSE**

SO HE DECIDED THE ONLY WAY TO ESCAPE WAS TO FIND A **DIFFERENT** STORY. A STORY WHICH WOULD EXPLAIN HOW HE GOT STUCK AND MAYBE, JUST **MAYBE** OFFER A WAY OUT.

SO THE CLOWN SAT DOWN TO SEARCH HIS MEMORY. WHICH IS WHERE THE PAST HIDES AND WHERE ALL STORIES COME FROM.

Vale of Tears

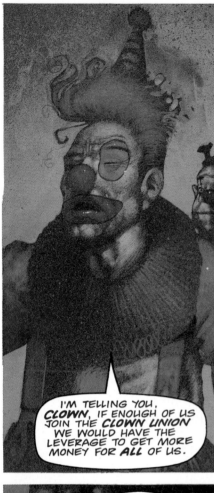

I'M TELLING YOU, *CLOWN*, IF ENOUGH OF US JOIN THE *CLOWN UNION* WE WOULD HAVE THE LEVERAGE TO GET MORE MONEY FOR *ALL* OF US.

BUT I DON'T *WANT* MORE MONEY.

SHEESH!

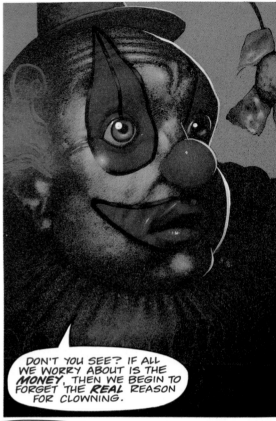

DON'T YOU SEE? IF ALL WE WORRY ABOUT IS THE *MONEY*, THEN WE BEGIN TO FORGET THE *REAL* REASON FOR CLOWNING.

AND WHAT'S THAT?

DON'T YOU KNOW? TO MAKE THE KIDS *LAUGH*, OF COURSE.

YOU KNOW, SOMETIMES, *ANGUS*, I THINK YOU'RE *PRETTY FUNNY* FOR A CLOWN. COME ON, I'LL BUY YOU A BEER AT THE CLOWN BAR.

THAT'S ALRIGHT, YOU GO AHEAD. I JUST HAVE A FEW THINGS I NEED TO CHECK OUT FIRST.

RIGHTY-O. SEE YOU IN THE BIG TOP.

YEAH, *RIGHTY-O*. (WHATTA SAP).

IT'S ABOUT TIME I **CRACKED** THIS CAPER WIDE OPEN!

--**ULP.** UH, **HI** GUYS. BOZO. FLOPPY. GEEZER. COCO. HOW'S TRICKS?

HEY **BOSS**, LOOK WHAT WEEZ FOUND SNOOPING OUTSIDE YUR TRAILER.

WELLLL...IF IT ISN'T MY **OLD FRIEND** ANGUS THE CLOWN. HOW NICE OF YOU TO DROP IN ON US.

OR SHOULD I SAY **DETECTIVE SERGEANT** ANGUS BRUMMER.

YOU REALLY DIDN'T THINK YOUR CRUDE ATTEMPTS AT DISGUISING YOURSELF AS ONE OF MY CLOWNS WOULD WORK DID YOU?

HHHUUUUHHHRRRRRR!

SHUT UP, TOBY, OR YOU'LL GET ANOTHER TASTE OF MY WHIP!

DON'T LOOK SO SURPRISED **DETECTIVE** BRUMMER. I'VE KNOWN ABOUT YOUR LITTLE RELATIONSHIP WITH TOBY FOR SOME TIME NOW. AND BELIEVE ME, THERE'S NOTHING I HATE MORE THAN A **STOOL-PONY.**

YOU'LL NEVER GET AWAY WITH THIS, **RINGMASTER.**

OH, BUT I WILL, BRUMMER, I **WILL.** AFTER ALL, WHO'S GOING TO STOP ME? YOU? TOBY? THE MARINES? *HAHAHAHAHAHAH!*

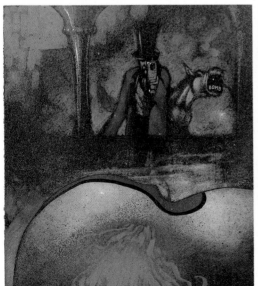

I'LL HEAR YOU LAUGH IN *HELL*, CLOWN!

KAAA-BOOOM!

DATA FOR NEW READERS

RO-JAWS... FEDERAL RE-CYCLING AND ENVIRONMENTAL DROID (*FRED 2L*)-- PROGRAMMED FOR CLEANING SEWERS, UNBLOCKING DRAINS AND GARBAGE DISPOSAL...

FAULTS IN THIS DROID'S OBEDIENCE AND LANGUAGE CIRCUITS -- PLUS GENERAL BAD BEHAVIOUR -- CAUSED HIM TO BE DISMISSED.

HAMMER-STEIN... WAR-DROID MARK THREE. HAD A DISTINGUISHED CAREER IN THE BIG WAR-- QUICKLY RISING TO SERGEANT... AND AWARDED MANY MEDALS...

AT THE END OF THE WAR, SOLDIER ROBOTS WERE NO LONGER NEEDED AND HE WAS DISCHARGED AS 'ARMY SURPLUS'.

RO-JAWS AND HAMMER-STEIN MET AT FLASH HARRY'S ROBO-MART AND BECAME CLOSE FRIENDS.

LOOK, COULD YOU MOVE A BIT AWAY FROM ME? NO WONDER THE CUSTOMERS WON'T BUY ME! THE SMELL FROM YOU --

WOTCHIT, MATE--I'M A SEWER ROBOT AND *PROUD* OF IT! I AIN'T SCARED OF *YOU*! I'LL TAKE YOU ON ANY DAY!

SECOND H[AND] BARGAI[N]

ARMY SURPLUS

ANY OFFERS?

THEN, SOME MONTHS LATER...

THE PUNTERS DON'T WANT SECOND HAND ROBOTS NO MORE--ESPECIALLY A COUPLE OF TIN *FREAKS* LIKE YOU TWO. YOU'RE GONNA BE *DESTROYED*!

TYPICAL! FLIPPIN' TYPICAL!

ENTER *HOWARD QUARTZ*, KNOWN AS MR. TEN PER-CENT, THE PARTLY HUMAN BOSS OF *RO-BUSTERS*...

WAIT! I'LL BUY THEM OFF YOU CHEAP. ROBOTS CAN DO THINGS WE *HUMANS* CAN'T--THEY'RE JUST WHAT I NEED FOR MY INTERNATIONAL RESCUE ORGANISATION --RO-BUSTERS!

AND SO THE TWO DROIDS JOINED RO-BUSTERS, WITH ITS HEADQUARTERS ON *DEVIL'S ISLAND*...

ROBOTS WERE THE PERFECT ANSWER TO THE DISASTERS OF THE TWENTY-FIRST CENTURY -- BECAUSE IT DIDN'T MATTER IF THEY "LIVED" OR "DIED" -- AT LEAST--*NOT TO HUMAN BEINGS!*

SO NOW ... AT THE SCENE OF THE TRAIN DISASTER ...

OUR JOB IS TO GET THIS **OXYGEN** DOWN TO THE CARRIAGES AT THE FRONT! MAYBE **I** OUGHT TO GO FIRST!

WADDYAMEAN? IT'S EASY FOR A SEWER ROBOT LIKE ME, WOT'S UNBLOCKED MORE "S" BENDS THAN YOU'VE KNOCKED OUT MACHINE GUN NESTS.

CAN'T WE CHANGE THE SUBJECT? YOU'RE ALWAYS GOING ON ABOUT **SEWAGE.**

WELL, I **LIKE** IT-- DON'T I? CAN'T HELP ME PROGRAMMING ... LOOK OUT, MATE ... **ANOTHER LANDSLIDE!**

THE DROIDS WERE BURIED BENEATH THOUSANDS OF TONS OF ROCK ...

KNOW SOMETHING, HAMMER-STEIN? WE'VE GOT TO GET OUT OF THIS BUSINESS!

KNOW SOMETHING, RO-JAWS? **YOU'RE RIGHT!**

WITH THE WAY ABOVE BLOCKED, THEY DUG DOWN TO THE TRAIN ...

YOO HOO!

NOW DON'T START SHOWING ME UP LIKE YOU USUALLY DO!

A ROBOT RESCUE TEAM ...THANK GOD! WE'RE SAVED!

WE'VE ONLY GOT AN HOUR'S SUPPLY OF AIR LEFT IN HERE... QUICK--GIVE US THOSE OXYGEN CYLINDERS!

HANG ABOUT! WE'VE ONLY GOT **NINE** CYLINDERS AND THERE'S **TEN** OF YOU, IN OTHER WORDS ... **ONE OF YOU** IS UP THE CREEK WITHOUT A PADDLE!

HAROLD...

WE'LL GET HAROLD OUT OF THE LUGGAGE COMPARTMENT --HE MIGHT MAKE THE LITTLE BOY FEEL *BETTER*! MEANWHILE, YOU LOT CAN DECIDE WHO IS GOING TO *VOLUNTEER*...

THIS REMINDS ME OF ONE OF THOSE "WHODUNNITS", HAMMER-STEIN... ONLY IT'S A "WHO-*GETS*-IT"!

LUGGAGE COMPARTMENT

I'VE NEVER *SEEN* SUCH COWARDLY HUMANS! IF I'D HAD THEM IN MY *OLD* REGIMENT...!

IN THE LUGGAGE COMPARTMENT...

RAISE YOU SIX.

WHAT A *HAND*! I GOT YOU POMMIE ROBOTS BEAT!

TATLER

CALL ME BRUCE

HELLO, COBBER-- I'M *BRUCE*... WANT IN ON A GAME?

YEAH, SURE, MATE!

CALL ME BR

OH NO, YOU DON'T... WE'VE GOT A *DISASTER* TO DEAL WITH!

EXCUSE ME... BUT IS *LITTLE MASTER* ALL RIGHT? I'VE BEEN SO *WORRIED*...!

YOU MUST BE HAROLD... WELL, I'M AFRAID HE'S COST A BIT OF *MOTION LOTION* --HE KEEPS *ASKING* FOR YOU.

OH, DEAR! I KNEW *BIG MASTER* SHOULD NEVER HAVE LOCKED ME IN THE LUGGAGE COMPARTMENT! IF... IF ANYTHING *HAPPENS* TO *LITTLE MASTER*--I SHALL NEVER *FORGIVE* MY-SELF... *NEVER*!

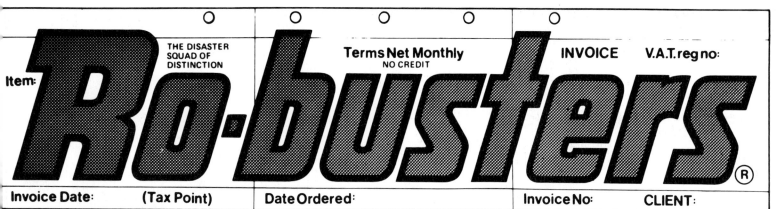

ONE OF THE SURVIVORS --MIKE MORGAN-- SNARLED GRIMLY...

THIS IS *RIDICULOUS*-- GIVING A *SEWER* *ROBOT* POWER OF LIFE AND DEATH!

HAVE YOU GOT A *BETTER* IDEA? NONE OF US IS WILLING TO DIE--SO A 'DROID HAS *GOT* TO CHOOSE! IT'S THE *ONLY WAY!*

IF YOU KNEW HOW *STUPID* YOU LOOKED, WEARING THAT WOMAN'S *WIG* AND *GOWN,* YOUR *WORSHIP...*!

WATCH YOUR-SELF, MUSH--I'M A *JUDGE*--SO I'M *ENTITLED* TO A BIT O' *RESPECT!* LET'S HEAR THE FIRST CASE!

I'M *LORD PETER WYNDIE*...A MAN OF GREAT WEALTH AND IMPORTANCE! I COULDN'T *POSSIBLY* VOLUNTEER TO DIE...

FANCY YERSELF, EH..?

LET'S SEE WHAT YER *ROBOT'S* GOT TO SAY FOR YOU ...*CALL THE FIRST WITNESS!*

CALL JAMES --LORD PETER WYNDIE'S ROBOT!

SURELY MY *WORD* IS GOOD ENOUGH! I *SWEAR* I'M TELLING THE *TRUTH!*

BUT ROBOTS ARE *PROGRAMMED* TO TELL THE TRUTH! THAT'S THE *FIRST LAW OF ROBOTICS,* MATE!

NOW, JAMES ...LET'S HAVE THE *LOW-DOWN* ON HIS NIBS!

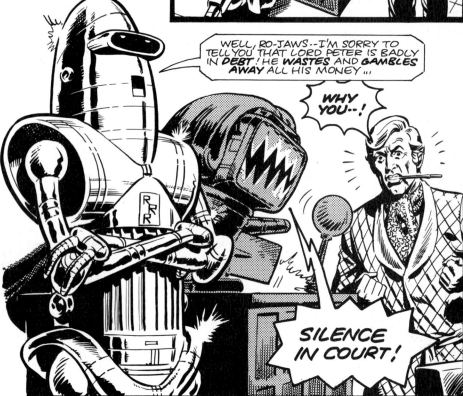

WELL, RO-JAWS--I'M SORRY TO TELL YOU THAT LORD PETER IS BADLY IN *DEBT!* HE *WASTES* AND *GAMBLES AWAY* ALL HIS MONEY...

WHY YOU--!

SILENCE IN COURT!

OH YES! HE BOUGHT ME ON HIRE PURCHASE, YOU KNOW,...AND HE'S BEHIND WITH MY PAYMENTS! I TOLD HIM ONLY LAST WEEK...IF HE DIDN'T PAY ALL THE ARREARS, I WOULD HAVE TO GO BACK TO THE SHOWROOM!

HIS LORDSHIP ONLY BOUGHT ME TO SHOW OFF...I'M A VERY EXPENSIVE ROBOT, CATERING FOR A SUPERIOR TYPE OF HUMAN...MY BODYWORK IS BY R.R. ROYCE...VOICE BY BONG AND OLAFSEN... ELECTRONICS BY HETOCHI... LOOK AT THIS FOR WORKMANSHIP!

BRILL, MATE... BRILL!

NEAT!

THEY DON'T MAKE ROBOTS LIKE YOU ANYMORE!

CAN WE GET ON WITH IT? WHILE YOU ROBOTS ARE ADMIRING EACH OTHER -- WE HUMANS ARE SUFFOCATING!

THE NEXT HUMAN WAS THE REVEREND STRANGEWAYS.

RECKON A VICAR SHOULD BE ALL RIGHT ...WHAT'S HIS ROBOT GOT TO SAY FOR HIM?

MY OWNER'S A GREAT GUY...BUT HE'S NOT REALLY A VICAR! THAT'S HIS DISGUISE! HE'S MAX THE CAT, ACE BURGLAR! OH, I DO LOVE GOING ON A JOB WITH HIM...!

ONE BY ONE, THE ROBOTS REVEALED THE HUMANS' SECRETS...

IT'S ALL COMING OUT NOW... ALL THE NITTY-GRITTY DETAILS ...EVERY 'DROID HAS DROPPED HIS OWNER RIGHT IN IT!

TROUBLE IS... ONE HUME IS JUST AS BAD AS THE NEXT! THEY'VE ALL GOT SOMETHING TO HIDE!

'HAROLD' -- MIKE MORGAN'S ROBOT -- BUZZED NERVOUSLY

I MUST TELL THE TRUTH ABOUT THE WAY YOU TREAT ME AND LITTLE MASTER, BIG MASTER. THE FIRST LAW OF ROBOTICS STATES WE ROBOTS CANNOT LIE!

YOU TRAITOR! THAT'LL FINISH ME!

WAIT! THE SECOND LAW OF ROBOTICS STATES A ROBOT MUST PROTECT HIS OWNERS! IF YOU TELL THE TRUTH, I'LL HURT LITTLE MASTER... REAL BAD!

OH, NO ...PLEASE!

NEXT WITNESS -- CALL HAROLD!

SO...

BIG MASTER IS A GOOD HUMAN. HE LOOKS AFTER HIS STEP-SON -- LITTLE MASTER -- VERY WELL. HE SEES THAT I AM WELL OILED AND HAVE REGULAR SERVICES EVERY THREE THOUSAND MILES.

FOR ONCE WE'VE HEARD ABOUT A HUME WHO IS A DECENT BLOKE! OKAY, HAROLD, YOU CAN STEP DOWN...

SUDDENLY...

NO, HAROLD -- YOU'RE LYING! SHOW THEM THE TRUTH! TAKE YOUR SHIRT OFF!

Droid Profile
Steve Parkhouse

Favourite Foods
1. Greek Salads
2. Seafood
3. Chocolate Hob-Nobs (plain)

Favourite Records
1. Girl at her Volcano
   - Ricky Lee Jones
2. Chicken Skin Music
   - Ry Cooder
3. Elgar's Enigma Variations
   and Allegro for Strings

Preferred Company on a Desert Island
Anybody but Madonna

Favourite 2000 AD Story
Anything by Alan Grant

Most Irritating Habit
Absent-Mindedness

Favourite Shop
Texas Superstore

Ideal Next President of the USA
Anybody but Madonna

Favourite Birthsign
Aquarius

Favourite Movies
1. The Seven Samurai
2. Blade Runner
3. Bringing Up Baby

Favourite Off-Duty Pastimes
Day dreaming, reading, hallucinating, etc.

Last Book Read
Quantum Healing by Deepak Chopra

Favourite Computer Game
The one that prints your name on very large cheques

Favourite Newspaper
Don't read 'em

Why?
I hate seeing the English language so badly mangled

Favourite Season of the Year
Spring

Favourite Figure in Terran History
Merlin

Tharg's Terror Tales

MEAT IS MEAT

GOOD EVENING, FEAR FREAKS. THARG THE ELDRITCH HERE, WITH ANOTHER YELP YARN FROM THE MIGHTY ONE'S CRYPT OF HORROR. LET ME TELL YOU THIS STORY AS IT WAS TOLD TO ME AND YOU'LL LEARN, AS I DID, THAT...

"I WAS ABOUT SIX WHEN IT HAPPENED. I SUPPOSE THE WHOLE THING WAS MY FAULT...

MOTEL

"IF I HADN'T ASKED DADDY TO STOP THE CAR SO I COULD LOOK AT THE ALLIGATOR FARM...

"BUT THEN, I WAS ONLY A CHILD...

2000 AD Credit Card
Script SYDNEY FALCO
Art MICK AUSTIN
Lettering ANNIE P

79

"HOW WAS I TO KNOW THERE WERE PEOPLE LIKE ...*THAT* IN THE WORLD?"

HELLOOO? LITTLE GIIIRL? WHERE ARE YOOOU?

"HE'D KILLED MY FATHER ALMOST IMMEDIATELY. SMASHED HIM ON THE BACK OF THE SKULL WITH A HEAVY WRENCH AND PUSHED HIM INTO THE *PIT*."

COME ON OUT. I'M NOT GOING TO *HURT* YOU...

"ONE OF THE ALLIGATORS HAD EATEN HIM WHOLE."

COME WITH UNCLE SYLVESTER AND SEE THE PRETTY ALLIGATORS ...

"HE'D CHASED MY MOTHER FOR ABOUT TWENTY MINUTES BEFORE HE FINALLY GOT HER WITH THAT PITCHFORK. HE FED HER TO HIS INFERNAL REPTILES, TOO.

"SHE JUST STOPPED SCREAMING A LITTLE WHILE AGO, HER MUFFLED CRIES FROM INSIDE THE ALLIGATOR'S GIZZARD FINALLY STILLED AS THE CREATURE'S DIGESTIVE SYSTEM WENT TO WORK.

" I KNEW THAT I DIDN'T WANT TO END UP THE SAME WAY.

"MY PLAN WAS TO GET TO THE HIGHWAY AND STOP THE FIRST CAR I SAW.

"THAT WAS IT.

"THE ONLY PROBLEM WAS THAT I HAD TO GET PAST *THE PIT* FIRST.

"AND THE ONLY WAY I THOUGHT I COULD DO THAT WAS TO *GO* FOR IT.

"SO I *DID*...

"'UNCLE SYLVESTER' MAY HAVE BEEN CRAZY BUT HE WASN'T *STUPID*.

AAH... DESSERT!

"HE'D BEEN WAITING FOR ME TO TRY THE OBVIOUS.

A TASTY LITTLE MEAT SNACKLET FOR MY PETS.

Droid Profile
John Ridgway

Favourite Foods
1. Cumberland sausage and chips
2. Moussaka
3. Ice cream (not on same plate)

Favourite Records
1. Silent ones
2. Silent ones
3. Silent ones

Preferred Company on a Desert Island
Frobisher the penguin

Favourite 2000 AD Story
Night Walker

Most Irritating Habit
Can't make up my mind

Favourite Shop
Any book shop

Ideal Next President of the USA
Lord Sutch

Favourite Birthsign
Taurus

Favourite Movies
1. Any Road Runner cartoon
2. Prince Valiant
3. Greystoke

Favourite Off-Duty Pastimes
Twiddling with a computer

Last Book Read
Labyrinth of the Night
by Bob Steele

Favourite Computer Game
Haven't got one

John Ridgway.

Favourite Newspaper
The Sun

Why?
Page 3

Favourite Season of the Year
Spring

Favourite Figure in Terran History
Attila the Hun

YEEEURRGH! GHOOAARRGH!

HMM. SOUNDS LIKE THE *STINGWORT*...

HEY, MAN! LIKE, STOP *SCREAMING*, MAN! REMEMBER THE CAMP APOCALYPSE MOTTO... "SO WHAT? IT'S NOT THE END OF THE WORLD".

"WE ARE ALSO LEARNING *BIRD IDENTIFICATION*..."

HEY, MAN! *OBSERVE* THAT INCREDIBLY TINY BIRD THAT IS JUST, LIKE, A *LITTLE SPECK* RIGHT UP IN THE *SKY*, MAN...

CAN ANYONE TELL ME WHAT KIND OF BIRD THAT *IS*?

N-NO, UNCLE WALDO.

FTAAM

RIGHT! IT IS OBVIOUSLY *TOTALLY IMPOSSIBLE* TO IDENTIFY A *MOVING* OBJECT FROM THAT FAR AWAY!

NOW, IF UNCLE *ERNEST* WILL HAND ME MY SPECIAL *BIRD-IDENTIFICATION EQUIPMENT*...

TH WUMP

OKAY! *NOW* WHO CAN TELL ME WHAT KIND OF BIRD THAT *IS*?

I-IT'S A *DEAD* BIRD, UNCLE WALDO.

S'RIGHT!

85

Droid Profile
Rian Hughes

Favourite Foods
1. Garlic Tortelloni
2. Mussels in cream and white wine sauce
3. Gateau Ganash (my mother's invention!)

Favourite Records
1. Yes Sir, I Can Boogie - Baccarah
2. How Soon is Now? - The Smiths
3. My Sex - Ultravox

Preferred Company on a Desert Island
The 15-piece Betty Boo All-Star Synchronised Swimming Co, Ltd

Favourite 2000 AD Story
Thunderhead Central (Progs 1021-1033)

Most Irritating Habit
Godlike perfection

Favourite Shop
Portobello Market

Ideal Next President of the USA
Jeff Koons

Favourite Birthsign
Scorpio

Favourite Movies
1. Dead Poet's Society
2. The Hairdresser's Husband
3. Blade Runner

Favourite Off-Duty Pastimes
The Bump, The Hustle, The Crazy Hand Jive

Last Book Read
Gödel, Escher, Bach by Douglas Hofstadter

Favourite Computer Game
Prince of Persia

Favourite Newspaper
Ealing Informer

Why?
Because the night belongs to love

Favourite Season of the Year
Up to age 21, winter - after age 21, summer

Favourite Figure in Terran History
Googol (one with a hundred noughts)

JUDGE DREDD YEARBOOK 1994

The GREATEST JUDGE DREDD YEARBOOK EVER! Some of the stunning contents include:

NEW 10-page MEAN MACHINE adventure, by JOHN WAGNER and MIKE McMAHON!

NEW 16-page JUDGE DREDD thriller, by ALAN GRANT and DEAN ORMSTON!

NEW 9-page DEVLIN WAUGH text story, by JOHN SMITH and SEAN PHILLIPS!

PLUS more STORIES, fascinating FEATURES and PIN-UPS!

ROGUE TROOPER

GIVE WAR A CHANCE

LOOK AT THEM! THERE MUST BE A HUNDRED NORT TROOPS OUT THERE!

MAYBE A THOUSAND!

WE HAVEN'T GOT A PRAYER, SCHROEDER!

WE'RE ON OUR OWN!

FUNNY THING FOR A PRIEST TO SAY, FATHER. COULDN'T YOU JUST HAVE A QUICK WORD WITH GOD AND GET US OUT OF THIS MESS?

HOW CAN YOU JOKE AT A TIME LIKE THIS, SCHROEDER, WHEN YOU KNOW WE'RE GOING TO DIE?

I'M NOT AFRAID TO DIE, FATHER...

NOT IF WE GO TO HEAVEN... LIKE YOU ALWAYS SAID WE WOULD!

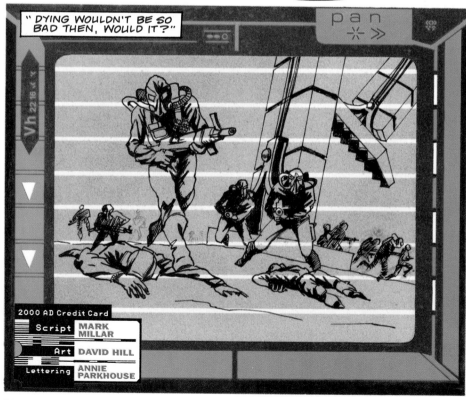

"DYING WOULDN'T BE SO BAD THEN, WOULD IT?"

pan

2000 AD Credit Card

Script MARK MILLAR

Art DAVID HILL

Lettering ANNIE PARKHOUSE

I CAN'T TAKE THIS! I CAN'T PRETEND ANYMORE...

BUTTON IT, FATHER.

THERE'S SOMETHING OUT THERE.

SOMETHING CHARGING THROUGH ALL THOSE NORT TROOPS!

PREPARE FOR AIR-BORNE ATTACK!

GET OUT OF HERE, ROGUE. THERE'S TOO MANY OF THEM!

BRAKKA BRAKKA

BRAKKA

DON'T LISTEN TO HIM, ROGUE.

GET IN SOME TARGET PRACTICE, BIG FELLA!

AIEEE!

IDIOT! DON'T LET HIM GET INTO THE DEEP WATER!

SWEEP THE AREA. CALL IN MORE GLIDERS!

IF THE G.I. GETS AWAY COMMANDER SLAUGHTERHOUSE WILL PICKLE OUR LIVERS!

98